# CHINESE NEW YEAR BEDTIME STORIES

Take your kid on a truly fascinating adventure with 20 stories celebrating Chinese New Year.

# - Table of Content -

# CHAPTER ONE

## Little Dragon Nicholas and the Joy of Sharing

Once upon a time, in the land of Chinese dragons, there lived a little dragon named Nicholas. He had a pink belly and a fluffy white beard, but what set him apart was his kind and generous heart.

Every year, as the Chinese New Year approached, Little Dragon Nicholas wanted to make the celebration extra special for all the dragons in his village. He had a brilliant idea – to create the most magnificent fireworks display they had ever seen.

However, there was a problem. Dragons were not very good at carrying all the materials needed to build such a grand fireworks show. The materials were too heavy, and they couldn't reach the high branches of the trees where colorful feathers for the fireworks' tails were hidden.

# Little Dragon Nicholas
# and the Joy of Sharing

But Nicholas was determined. He knew that with a little help from his friends, they could make it happen. So, he went to the nearby forest where the Joyful Birds lived, and he kindly asked them for their colorful feathers.

Next, he visited the Magical Unicorn Luna, who gave him a special, sparkling dust to make the fireworks even more enchanting.

To transport all the materials, Humble Turtle Zephyr offered his slow but steady help. Together, they built a magnificent ramp to launch the fireworks high into the sky.

On the night of the Chinese New Year, all the dragons and forest creatures gathered to watch the breathtaking fireworks display. It was a sight to behold, and everyone was filled with joy and wonder.

# Little Dragon Nicholas
# and the Joy of Sharing

Little Dragon Nicholas realized that by working together and being generous, they had created something truly magical. The celebration was more splendid than ever before, and he learned that cooperation and kindness lead to happiness.

Cooperation and generosity lead to happiness, and when we work together, we can create something truly wonderful.

# CHAPTER TWO

## Joyful Harmony and the Dance of Balance

In a distant land, during the grand Chinese New Year celebration, there lived a creature named Joyful Harmony. Joyful Harmony was a graceful and colorful bird with wings that sparkled like rainbows, and she was known throughout the kingdom for her remarkable sense of balance.

Every year, during the New Year festivities, Joyful Harmony would perform a special dance. It was a dance that showcased her perfect balance, as she gracefully balanced on a thin bamboo pole.

One day, as she was practicing her dance, she noticed that her balance wasn't as perfect as it used to be. She was wobbling and struggling to maintain her poise. This troubled her deeply because her dance was a symbol of harmony and balance in life.

# Joyful Harmony and the Dance of Balance

She decided to seek the advice of Wise Old Tortoise, who was known for his wisdom and experience. Wise Old Tortoise listened carefully to Joyful Harmony's concerns and said, "My dear friend, balance in life is like a delicate dance. Sometimes, we may lose our balance, but it's essential to remember that it's okay. The key is to find it again and keep moving forward."

With Wise Old Tortoise's words in her heart, Joyful Harmony continued to practice her dance, embracing the moments of imbalance as opportunities to improve. As the Chinese New Year approached, she performed her dance for the kingdom.

Her dance was a stunning display of beauty and grace, but what made it truly remarkable was the lesson it taught. Joyful Harmony showed that even when life throws us off balance, we can always find our way back and continue the dance of life with joy and harmony.

# Joyful Harmony and the Dance of Balance

Maintaining balance in life is like a delicate dance, and it's okay to wobble sometimes. The key is to find your balance again and keep moving forward with joy and harmony.

# CHAPTER THREE

## The Cheerful Panda Ping

Once upon a time, in a lush bamboo forest nestled between green mountains, there lived a delightful panda named Ping. Ping was known far and wide for her radiant smile, which could brighten even the cloudiest of days.

In the heart of the bamboo forest, where the animals all called each other friends, there was a special tree known as the "Happiness Tree." It was said that when someone was feeling down or the forest seemed gloomy, the Happiness Tree would lose its leaves. Ping had always wondered if this magical tree truly existed.

One overcast day, the animals of the forest woke up feeling a bit sad. The sky was gray, and a gentle rain began to fall. Ping knew it was the perfect time to find the Happiness Tree and put its magic to the test.

# The Cheerful Panda Ping

With her smile as radiant as ever, Ping set off on a quest through the bamboo forest, following her heart and spreading joy wherever she went. She told funny stories, danced silly dances, and even shared some of her bamboo treats with her friends. As Ping brought laughter and happiness to the forest, something magical started to happen.

Ping and her friends stumbled upon a magnificent tree with leaves as bright as the sun. It was the Happiness Tree! The leaves fluttered and shone in the rain, and a gentle warmth filled the air. Ping's smile had indeed worked its magic, and the tree responded to her joy and kindness.

The animals were overjoyed and realized that Ping's smile had a magical power to make not only the forest but also their hearts bloom with happiness. From that day forward, whenever someone in the bamboo forest felt sad, they would seek out Ping's cheerful presence, knowing that her smile had the power to chase away any gloom.

# The Cheerful Panda Ping

Smile has a magical power. When you smile and share your joy, you can bring happiness to those around you and make the world a brighter place. So, my dear child, always remember the magic of a smile and share it with others.

# CHAPTER FOUR

## The Enchanting Fish Rina

In a shimmering pond surrounded by vibrant flowers and tall reeds, there lived a magical fish named Rina. Rina was no ordinary fish; her scales sparkled like precious gems, and her tail shimmered with all the colors of the rainbow. But what truly made Rina special was her generous heart.

One sunny day, Rina noticed that some of the other fish in the pond were feeling hungry and tired. The food supply was running low, and there was not enough for everyone to eat. Rina couldn't bear to see her friends in distress, so she decided to share her food with them.

Every day, Rina would swim to the farthest corners of the pond, searching for the juiciest worms and the plumpest insects. She would then bring her delicious finds to her friends, ensuring that no one went hungry. Rina's selflessness filled the pond with happiness and gratitude.

# The Enchanting Fish Rina

As days turned into weeks, something miraculous began to happen. The more Rina shared, the more the pond seemed to flourish. The flowers around the pond grew taller and more colorful, and the water sparkled even brighter. Rina's generous heart was somehow making the whole pond come to life.

One night, as the Chinese New Year approached, a beautiful golden fish-shaped lantern descended from the sky and gently floated on the water's surface. It was a symbol of good fortune and blessings. The pond had been transformed into a magical and enchanting place because of Rina's generosity.

The other fish realized that Rina's selflessness had not only brought them food but also an abundance of beauty and joy. They thanked Rina for her kindness and learned that sharing not only warms the hearts of others but also brings happiness and prosperity to all.

# The Enchanting Fish Rina

Worth being generous and sharing. Just like Rina, when you give from your heart, not only do you bring joy to others, but you also create a more beautiful and prosperous world for everyone. So, my dear child, remember the magic of generosity, and may your dreams be filled with the sparkle and beauty of Rina's pond.

# CHAPTER FIVE

## The Living Statue Shi

In a quaint village nestled between rolling hills, there stood an ancient temple with a remarkable statue named Shi. The statue was made of pure white marble and depicted a young girl with a serene expression. But there was something truly extraordinary about this statue—it had the power to come to life.

Shi had been a living girl once, but a long time ago, she had been transformed into a statue by a powerful sorcerer. She could only come to life for a short time during the Chinese New Year, and her greatest joy was to spend that time with her friends in the village.

Every year, as the Chinese New Year approached, the villagers eagerly awaited the moment when Shi would come to life. They would prepare a grand celebration, decorating the temple and making delicious treats. Shi's friends, especially two young children named Mei and Ming, were always overjoyed to see her.

# The Living Statue Shi

One Chinese New Year's Eve, as the clock struck midnight, Shi's statue began to glow softly, and she came to life. Mei and Ming ran to the temple, their faces filled with excitement and happiness. They held hands with Shi and danced under the lantern-lit sky.

As the night went on, Shi and her friends enjoyed the festivities, shared stories, and laughed together. But as the first rays of the morning sun touched the horizon, Shi knew her time as a living statue was coming to an end. She returned to her marble form, and her friends said their goodbyes, their hearts filled with love and gratitude.

The villagers had learned that true friendship was priceless, and they cherished the moments they spent with Shi during each Chinese New Year. They realized that even though she could only be with them for a short time, the bond they shared was unbreakable.

# The Living Statue Shi

True friendship is priceless. Just like Shi and her friends, when you have friends who love and cherish you, you have something precious that cannot be measured in riches or time. So, my dear child, value your friendships and the moments you spend together, for they are truly invaluable.

# CHAPTER SIX

## The Friendly Tiger Chang

In a lush jungle, where tall trees swayed in the breeze, there lived a kind-hearted tiger named Chang. Chang was not like other tigers; he was gentle and friendly, and he loved making new friends in the jungle.

One sunny day, while Chang was exploring the jungle, he heard a faint cry for help. Following the sound, he found a young monkey named Milo stuck high up in a tree. Milo had climbed too high and was now too scared to come down.

Without hesitation, Chang offered his help. With his strong and agile body, he climbed the tree and reached Milo. Chang reassured the frightened monkey and gently carried him down to safety. Milo was grateful and happy to have made a new friend in Chang.

# The Friendly Tiger Chang

From that day on, Chang and Milo became inseparable friends. They explored the jungle together, shared stories, and laughed under the golden sun. Chang showed Milo the beauty of the jungle, and Milo taught Chang the joy of swinging through the trees.

But one stormy night, a fierce thunderstorm struck the jungle, and Chang and Milo found themselves trapped in a cave. The rain poured, and the thunder roared, making Milo shiver with fear. Chang, however, comforted Milo, telling him stories and making him feel safe.

As the night passed, the storm subsided, and the first rays of dawn broke through the clouds. Chang and Milo emerged from the cave, their friendship stronger than ever. They realized that friends were there to support and comfort each other in times of need.

# The Friendly Tiger Chang

Friends are a source of support in difficult times. Just like Chang and Milo, when you have true friends, you know that they will be there for you when you need them the most, offering comfort and strength. So, my dear child, treasure your friendships, for they are like a shelter in life's storms.

# CHAPTER SEVEN

## The Friendly Dog Bao

In a cozy little neighborhood, there lived a friendly dog named Bao . Bao was known throughout the town for his wagging tail and his ever-welcoming bark. He loved to make new friends and was always ready to lend a paw to those in need.

One bright morning, as Bao was chasing his tail in the backyard, he heard a faint whimper coming from the nearby woods. Curious and concerned, he followed the sound and found a lost kitten named Kiki. Kiki was scared and alone, with no idea how to find her way back home.

Bao approached Kiki with a gentle woof and a friendly wag of his tail. He offered to help Kiki find her way back to her family. With Bao leading the way, Kiki felt safe and began to trust her new friend.

# The Friendly Dog Bao

Together, Bao  and Kiki embarked on an adventure through the woods. Bao  sniffed the ground and followed the scents, while Kiki stayed close to him. They crossed bubbling streams, climbed gentle hills, and even shared their stories along the way.

As the day turned into evening, they finally reached Kiki's home. Her family was overjoyed to see her, and Kiki thanked Bao  for his loyalty and kindness. Bao  wagged his tail with happiness and returned to his own home, knowing he had made a true friend in Kiki.

From that day on, Bao  and Kiki were inseparable. They played together, ate together, and slept side by side. Their bond grew stronger with each passing day, and they realized that loyalty and friendship were the most precious gifts of all.

# The Friendly Dog Bao

Loyalty and friendship are priceless. Just like Bao and Kiki, when you have friends who are loyal and stand by your side, you have something that cannot be measured in riches or possessions. So, my dear child, cherish your friendships and be a loyal friend in return, for true friends are a treasure beyond compare.

# CHAPTER EIGHT

## The Clever Fox Leo

Once upon a time, in a peaceful forest, there lived a clever fox named Leo. Leo was known throughout the forest for his quick wit and cunning ways. He could always find a solution to any problem, but sometimes he used his cleverness for mischief.

One sunny morning, Leo overheard the animals of the forest talking about a Chinese New Year celebration that was going to take place. Leo was excited about the festivities but couldn't resist the idea of tricking his friends.

He approached the other animals and said,

"I've heard that the Chinese New Year will bring great fortune to those who wear their socks inside out on the first day of the celebration."

# The Clever Fox Leo

The animals, not suspecting Leo's trickery, quickly turned their socks inside out and went about their day. Leo chuckled to himself, thinking he had outsmarted everyone.

But as the day went on, Leo saw that his friends were becoming increasingly uncomfortable with their socks inside out. They stumbled and tripped, and their discomfort grew. Leo realized that he had played a mean trick on them.

Feeling guilty, Leo approached his friends and confessed to his mischievous deed. He apologized sincerely and helped them fix their socks. Leo learned that his cleverness should be used for good, not to play tricks on others.

The animals forgave Leo and appreciated his honesty. They continued to enjoy the Chinese New Year festivities together, with Leo using his cleverness to make the celebration even more enjoyable.

# The Clever Fox Leo

Always be honest and truthful. Just like Leo, when we are honest with our friends and admit our mistakes, we can mend any hurt feelings and continue to enjoy each other's company. So, my dear child, remember to be truthful and use your cleverness for good, for honesty is a virtue that makes friendships stronger.

# CHAPTER NINE

## The Playful Meadow Pony Sam

In a picturesque meadow, under the gentle warmth of the sun, there lived a playful pony named Sam. Sam loved to gallop and jump around the meadow, enjoying the freedom of the open field. He believed that movement and play were essential for a healthy and happy life.

Every day, Sam would invite his animal friends to join him in games of tag, races, and playful leaps. They all laughed and had a great time, their spirits lifted by the joy of play. Sam knew that staying active and having fun were good for their bodies and minds.

# The Playful Meadow Pony Sam

One sunny morning, as the Chinese New Year approached, Sam noticed that his friends seemed tired and gloomy. They were so busy preparing for the celebration that they had forgotten the importance of play.

Sam decided to remind them about the value of movement and fun. He organized a playful parade through the meadow, with dancing, games, and laughter. His friends couldn't resist joining in, and soon, their weariness disappeared, replaced by smiles and energy.

As they celebrated together, Sam's friends realized that play was not just enjoyable but also essential for their well-being. They thanked Sam for reminding them to stay active and have fun, especially during the festive season.

# The Playful Meadow Pony Sam

Movement and play are important for health. Just like Sam and his friends, when we make time for play and physical activity, we not only have fun but also keep our bodies and minds healthy. So, my dear child, remember to stay active and enjoy the pleasures of play, for it brings happiness and good health.

# CHAPTER TEN

## The Sad Bear Norbert

In a quiet forest nestled between tall trees, there lived a bear named Norbert. Norbert was known throughout the forest for his gloomy demeanor. He always seemed to have a cloud of sadness hanging over him, and he often felt like life was too complicated.

One sunny day, as the Chinese New Year approached, Norbert watched the other animals in the forest preparing for the celebration. They were decorating their homes with colorful lanterns, practicing their dance moves, and baking delicious treats.

Norbert felt even sadder as he thought about how he couldn't find joy in such festivities. He believed that happiness was too complex and unreachable for him. He roamed the forest with a heavy heart, unable to join in the joy of the approaching new year.

# The Sad Bear Norbert

But as he wandered deeper into the forest, Norbert stumbled upon a quiet clearing. In the middle of that clearing, he noticed a simple, beautiful wildflower swaying in the breeze. Its bright colors and delicate petals captivated him.

Norbert sat down beside the wildflower and watched it dance in the wind. He realized that happiness didn't always have to come from grand celebrations or complicated things. Sometimes, joy could be found in the simplest and most ordinary of moments, like the beauty of a wildflower.

As Norbert sat there, his heart began to feel lighter, and a faint smile crossed his face. He had found a moment of happiness in the simplest of things, and it made him realize that he could find joy in life, even amidst his sadness.

# The Sad Bear Norbert

We should seek joy in simple things. Just like Norbert, when we appreciate the beauty and happiness in everyday moments, life becomes more fulfilling and meaningful. So, my dear child, remember to find joy in the simple things around you, for they hold the key to happiness.

# CHAPTER ELEVEN

## The Noble Elephant Stan

In a vast and green jungle, there lived a noble elephant named Stan. Stan was known throughout the jungle for his courage and kindness. He believed that nobility and bravery were important values to uphold.

One day, as the Chinese New Year approached, a group of animals came to Stan with a problem. They told him about a fierce and menacing tiger that had been causing fear and havoc in the jungle. The other animals were afraid and didn't know what to do.

Stan knew that it was his duty to protect his fellow jungle dwellers. With a determined heart, he set off to find the tiger and bring peace back to the jungle. He marched deep into the forest, his large ears picking up the faintest sounds.

# The Noble Elephant Stan

After a long and arduous journey, Stan found the tiger hiding in a cave. The tiger growled and roared, but Stan stood tall and spoke to him with kindness and understanding. He learned that the tiger was only acting out of fear and anger.

Stan shared stories of unity and friendship from the jungle, and the tiger's heart began to soften. Stan offered the tiger a chance to change and be a part of the jungle's community. The tiger, touched by Stan's nobility and courage, agreed to give peace a chance.

Together, Stan and the tiger returned to the jungle, surprising the other animals with their newfound friendship. Stan's act of bravery and kindness had not only brought peace to the jungle but also taught everyone the value of nobility and courage.

# The Noble Elephant Stan

Nobility and courage are important values. Just like Stan, when we stand up for what is right and face challenges with bravery and kindness, we can bring about positive change and inspire others to do the same. So, my dear child, remember the importance of being noble and courageous in life's adventures.

# CHAPTER TWELVE

## The Cheerful Snake Victoria

In a vibrant garden, where flowers swayed to a gentle breeze, there lived a cheerful snake named Victoria. Victoria was known throughout the garden for her bright spirit and her unshakable optimism. She believed that staying positive was the key to overcoming challenges.

One sunny morning, as the Chinese New Year approached, Victoria noticed that her animal friends in the garden were feeling down. The flowers were not blooming as they should, and a gray cloud seemed to hang over everything. Her friends were worried and sad.

# The Cheerful Snake Victoria

Victoria, determined to spread some cheer, decided to organize a colorful celebration to lift everyone's spirits. She gathered vibrant flowers, painted colorful banners, and invited all her friends to join in the festivities.

As the celebration began, the garden transformed into a lively and joyful place. Victoria and her friends danced, sang, and shared stories. They laughed under the golden sun, and slowly, the gray cloud began to disappear.

Victoria's optimism was contagious, and her friends couldn't help but smile and enjoy the moment. They realized that, with a positive attitude, even the darkest days could become bright and cheerful.

# The Cheerful Snake Victoria

Optimism helps overcome difficulties. Just like Victoria, when you stay positive and optimistic, you can face challenges with courage and turn them into opportunities for joy and growth. So, my dear child, remember the power of optimism and the ability to brighten the world around you. Goodnight, and may your dreams be filled with the vibrant colors and laughter of Victoria's garden celebration.

# CHAPTER THIRTEEN

## The Optimistic Eagle Oscar

In a vast and open sky, there lived an optimistic eagle named Oscar. Oscar was known throughout the skies for his unwavering self-belief and his understanding that having faith in oneself could lead to great success.

One bright morning, as the Chinese New Year approached, Oscar noticed that many of the birds in the sky were feeling down and doubting their abilities. They thought they couldn't fly as high or as gracefully as he could.

Oscar wanted to share his optimism and inspire his fellow birds to believe in themselves. He organized a soaring competition, inviting all the birds to participate. The goal was to see who could fly the highest and the most gracefully.

# The Optimistic Eagle Oscar

The birds hesitated at first, feeling unsure of themselves, but Oscar's words of encouragement and belief in their abilities motivated them to take part. The competition began, and as the birds spread their wings, something incredible happened.

One by one, they started to fly higher and more gracefully than they ever thought possible. Oscar cheered them on from the sidelines, reminding them that their self-belief was the key to their success.

The birds soared through the sky, and the once-doubtful atmosphere was filled with confidence and determination. They reached heights they had never imagined, and the joy of their accomplishment lifted their spirits.

In the end, all the birds felt a sense of pride and self-assurance that they had never experienced before. Oscar's optimism had shown them that with faith in themselves, they could achieve remarkable feats.

# The Optimistic Eagle Oscar

Believing in oneself leads to success. Just like Oscar and the birds, when we have confidence in our abilities and believe in ourselves, we can accomplish great things and reach new heights. So, my dear child, remember the power of self-belief, for it is the key to unlocking your full potential.

# CHAPTER FOURTEEN

## The Wise Monkey Max

In a lush jungle, where ancient trees whispered secrets, there lived a wise monkey named Max. Max was known throughout the jungle for his boundless wisdom and his belief in the value of knowledge. He understood that wisdom and knowledge were precious treasures.

One tranquil morning, as the Chinese New Year approached, Max noticed that some of the animals in the jungle were struggling with challenges they faced. They felt stuck and didn't know how to overcome their problems.

Max, eager to share his wisdom, gathered the animals and offered to teach them valuable lessons and knowledge.

# The Wise Monkey Max

He organized a jungle school where he shared his wisdom about navigating the jungle, finding food, and solving problems.

The animals eagerly attended Max's lessons, and as they learned, their confidence grew. They began to see solutions to their problems and felt more capable and empowered.

As the days passed, the jungle became a place of growth and learning. The animals realized that with wisdom and knowledge, they could face any challenge that came their way.

Max's lessons had not only enriched their minds but also strengthened their bonds as a community. They celebrated their newfound wisdom and the importance of sharing knowledge.

# The Wise Monkey Max

Wisdom and knowledge are valuable. Just like Max and the jungle animals, when we seek wisdom and knowledge, we can face life's challenges with confidence and find solutions to problems that may seem insurmountable. So, my dear child, remember the value of learning and the power of knowledge, for they are treasures that enrich our lives.

# CHAPTER FIFTEEN

## The Humble Tortoise Zephyr

Once upon a time, in a lush, green forest, there lived a humble tortoise named Zephyr. Zephyr was a slow but steady tortoise who always took his time to do things right. While all the other animals in the forest were busy rushing around, Zephyr moved at his own pace.

One sunny day, the animals heard about a race to celebrate the Chinese New Year. They were all excited and started practicing immediately. Zephyr, too, decided to participate. He practiced every day, slowly and steadily, while the other animals laughed at his slowness.

Finally, the day of the race arrived. The animals lined up at the starting line, ready to sprint to the finish. Zephyr, however, stood there patiently. The race began, and all the animals rushed ahead, leaving Zephyr behind. But he didn't lose hope. He kept moving forward, step by step, at his own pace.

# The Humble Tortoise Zephyr

As the other animals tired themselves out, they began to slow down and take breaks. Zephyr, on the other hand, continued to move steadily. Slowly but surely, he passed one animal after another. And when the finish line was in sight, Zephyr crossed it, winning the race!

The other animals were astonished. They realized that Zephyr's patience and perseverance had paid off. They had rushed and tired themselves out, but Zephyr had reached the finish line calmly and triumphantly.

Patience and perseverance lead to success. It doesn't matter if you're slow or fast; what matters is that you keep moving forward with determination and never give up on your goals. Just like Zephyr, you can achieve great things through patience and hard work. So, remember, my dear child, sometimes, slow and steady wins the race.

# CHAPTER SIXTEEN

## The Hardworking Rabbit Kajetan

Once upon a time, in a peaceful meadow, there lived a hardworking rabbit named Kajetan. Kajetan loved to spend his days hopping around the meadow, but he also knew the importance of working diligently.

One day, Kajetan heard about the Chinese New Year festival and wanted to contribute something special to the celebration. He decided to plant a beautiful garden of colorful flowers that would bloom in time for the festivities. Kajetan worked tirelessly, digging the soil, planting seeds, and watering them every day.

As the days passed, Kajetan's garden started to grow. He cared for his plants with love and dedication, making sure they had everything they needed to thrive. He even sang cheerful songs to them as he worked.

# The Hardworking Rabbit Kajetan

Finally, the Chinese New Year arrived, and Kajetan's garden was in full bloom, with vibrant flowers of all colors. The other animals in the meadow were amazed by the beauty of his garden and praised Kajetan for his hard work and determination.

During the festival, Kajetan's garden became the centerpiece of the celebration, bringing joy and happiness to everyone. Kajetan felt proud of his efforts and was filled with a sense of accomplishment.

Hard work always pays off. Just like Kajetan, when you put in effort and dedication into something, you can achieve remarkable results. So, my dear child, remember that your hard work and perseverance can bring beauty and happiness to your life and the lives of others.

# CHAPTER SEVENTEEN

## The Creative Chameleon Camille

In a colorful forest, where every hue imaginable danced in the leaves, there lived a creative chameleon named Camille. Camille was known throughout the forest for her vivid imagination and her ability to express herself in the most unique ways. She believed that self-expression and imagination were the keys to a vibrant life.

One day, as the Chinese New Year approached, Camille noticed that her animal friends in the forest were feeling a bit dull and uninspired. The vibrant colors of the forest seemed to have faded, and her friends were longing for something new and exciting.

Camille, with her creative spirit, decided to bring a burst of color and inspiration to the forest. She began to paint colorful murals on the tree trunks, created sculptures from fallen leaves, and even organized a whimsical costume parade for her friends.

# The Creative Chameleon Camille

As the forest came alive with Camille's creativity, her friends couldn't help but be inspired. They joined in the fun, adding their own artistic touches to the surroundings. The forest transformed into a magical place filled with unique expressions of imagination.

Camille's message was clear: everyone had a creative spark within them, waiting to be ignited. Her friends realized that self-expression and imagination were not only enjoyable but also essential for a fulfilling life.

We should express ourselves and nurture our imagination. Just like Camille, when we let our creativity flow and express ourselves in unique ways, we can bring color and inspiration to our lives and the world around us. So, my dear child, remember the importance of self-expression and imagination, for they are the keys to a vibrant and fulfilling life.

# CHAPTER EIGHTEEN

## The Hardworking Bee Patricia

In a bustling meadow filled with colorful blooms, there lived a hardworking bee named Patricia. Patricia was known throughout the meadow for her diligence and her belief in the power of teamwork. She knew that working together could bring great benefits.

One sunny morning, as the Chinese New Year approached, Patricia noticed that the flowers in the meadow were drooping and needed nourishment. She knew that she couldn't do it all on her own, so she gathered her fellow bees and proposed a plan to collect nectar and pollen together to revitalize the flowers.

The other bees eagerly agreed, and they set off on their mission. Each bee had a role to play, from collecting nectar to spreading pollen. They worked in harmony, their buzzing wings creating a symphony of cooperation.

# The Hardworking Bee Patricia

As the days passed, the meadow began to flourish once more. The flowers stood tall and vibrant, and the meadow was filled with the sweet scent of blooming blossoms. The bees knew that their hard work and teamwork had made it all possible.

Patricia and her fellow bees celebrated their success with a joyful dance in the meadow. They realized that by working together, they could achieve more than they ever could alone.

Teamwork brings benefits. Just like Patricia and her team of bees, when we collaborate and work together towards a common goal, we can achieve great things and create positive changes in our world. So, my dear child, remember the importance of teamwork and cooperation, for together, we can accomplish remarkable feats.

# CHAPTER NINETEEN

## The Flying Unicorn Luna

In a magical forest, there lived a special unicorn named Luna. Luna had a big dream – she wished she could fly among the stars. Every night, she would gaze up at the sky and imagine herself soaring through the night, touching the twinkling stars.

One day, Luna decided to make her dream come true. She believed in herself and her dream with all her heart. She began to practice diligently, running and jumping higher and higher each day, trying to reach the sky.

With each leap, Luna felt herself getting lighter, and her hooves barely touched the ground. One beautiful night, under the light of the full moon, Luna took a mighty jump and felt herself soaring higher and higher. She had become a flying unicorn, and her dream had come true!

# The Flying Unicorn Luna

Luna danced among the stars, leaving a trail of glittering stardust behind her. She felt the cool night breeze on her face as she flew through the night sky. Luna realized that her belief in herself and her dream had made the impossible possible.

Dreams can come true if you believe in them. Just like Luna, when you have a dream and truly believe in it, you can accomplish incredible things. So, my dear child, always have faith in your dreams and yourself, and one day, you'll soar among the stars just like Luna.

# CHAPTER TWENTY

## The Adorable Kitty Kailani

Once upon a time, in a cozy little town, there lived a charming kitty named Kailani. Kailani was known throughout the town for her fluffy fur and bright, sparkling eyes. She was the prettiest cat anyone had ever seen.

One sunny day, a fancy cat competition was announced in the town. All the cats were excited and started getting ready, grooming their fur and wearing fancy accessories. Kailani, however, didn't join in the frenzy. She believed that beauty came from within and didn't want to change who she was just to win a competition.

The day of the competition arrived, and all the cats paraded in front of the judges, showing off their looks. Kailani simply walked up to the judges and purred with warmth and kindness. The judges were charmed by her inner beauty and awarded her the title of the "Most Beautiful Heart."

# The Adorable Kitty Kailani

The other cats were surprised and realized that Kailani had shown them that true beauty came from kindness, love, and a caring heart, not just outer appearances.


Beauty is on the inside, not the outside. Just like Kailani, when you are kind, loving, and compassionate, you become truly beautiful. So, my dear child, remember that it's what's in your heart that matters most, and being a kind and loving person makes you the most beautiful of all.

# Dear Readers,

Our team would like to thank you sincerely for purchasing our Chinese New Year Bedtime Stories. Your support and interest in our work are extremely important and inspiring to us.

Your feedback is valuable to us, so We would like to ask you to share your thoughts about the book on the Amazon platform. Your honest reviews will help us better understand what your opinion is about our book and what elements can be improved or changed in the future.

We greatly appreciate every comment, whether it is positive or negative. Your feedback will help other readers make an informed choice when purchasing a book.

Best regards,

Team Kei W. Noya

Made in the USA
Las Vegas, NV
28 January 2024

85045990R00036